David Bradshaw is one of the baby boomers from parents still celebrating the end of the war. Born in Stamford in 1947, the family moved to the country when he was 11 years old. He spent his working life in financial services, with a hobby of penning children's silly poems.
Once retired, he set about publishing them as a joint venture with his daughter, Lisa, doing the artwork. Her skills bring the animals to life, portraying their medical problems in a humorous way.

Lisa was born in Peterborough in 1972. She developed a wanderlust, meeting her husband, Phil, in Jordan, where he was running a sailing school.
They spent several years crewing a commercial yacht together, taking small groups around the Caribbean. Phil was responsible for the sailing, while Lisa used her skills as a chef.
She now lives in Stamford, where she home-schools their 9-year-old daughter, runs an online shop selling eco-friendly, ethically sourced products, and owns and runs, in partnership with a friend, a craft and community centre.
She has many creative talents, not least her art work, as illustrated in this book.

TOOTH MOUTH FANG BEAK

Written by
David Bradshaw

illustrated by
Lisa Johnson

AUSTIN MACAULEY PUBLISHERS™
LONDON • CAMBRIDGE • NEW YORK • SHARJAH

A CIP catalogue record for this title is available from the British Library.

ISBN 9781398411517 (Paperback)
ISBN 9781398411524 (ePub e-book)

www.austinmacauley.com

First Published 2021
Austin Macauley Publishers Ltd®
1 Canada Square, Canary Wharf
London, E14 5AA
+44 (0)20 7038 8212
+44 (0)20 3515 0352

Once King

Still fearless, brave, his ragged mane,
this once proud prince wears mangey fleece.
He was a king in more than name,
before he lost his precious teeth.

His span, not great in lion years,
this beast, he sits here near to tears.
His roar erupts more like a croak,
due to his undernourished throat.

His prey once caught, escapes
and runs;
he cannot kill it with his gums.
The shame he hides down deep beneath,
to cover up his lack of teeth.

His once proud roar would fear instil,
all lands he sees were his alone.
Now others pinch his wives at will,
this chills his marrow to the bone.

His snarl meant death, he'd
never miss,
now all you get's a gummy kiss!
Into a rage he is easily goaded,
now his last molars overloaded.

If only when that he was youthful,
his mouth afresh and still was toothfull,
he'd listened to his wise old mother -
"Clean your teeth though it's a bother!"

11

"Your teeth get covered with
dirt and dust,
to clean with brush and
paste you must.
If you don't, you will rue the day".
He remembers well how
she would say.

Emilina

So thin she was that her demeanour,
was pained and sad, our Emilina.
A pig of such minute dimension,
of social standing, she'd no pretension.

Her mouth it was that hurt and ached;
to chew her food no hunger slaked.
The problem was her dental caries;
her tooth she wished would see the fairies.

14

With breath so bad, was not befriended;

there was a time she was intended.

She felt alone and introverted;

friend and lover had her deserted.

Her Mum and Dad and all her closest
could not stand her halitosis.
In fields she stands, this lonely swine;
her jaw doth pain, her heart doth pine.

To sweet her breath and ease her pain,
win back her friends and feed her frame,
she WILL seek out the dentist's name
who'll cure her ills and stop her shame.

The Snake

His skin is cold, his body strong;
strikes so quick with reach so long.
One bite and he will firmly hang
on with his last remaining fang.

No legs or feet he needs to run,
to have him chase you is no fun.
He moves with hiss and slide and slip,
to catch you in his fatal grip.

19

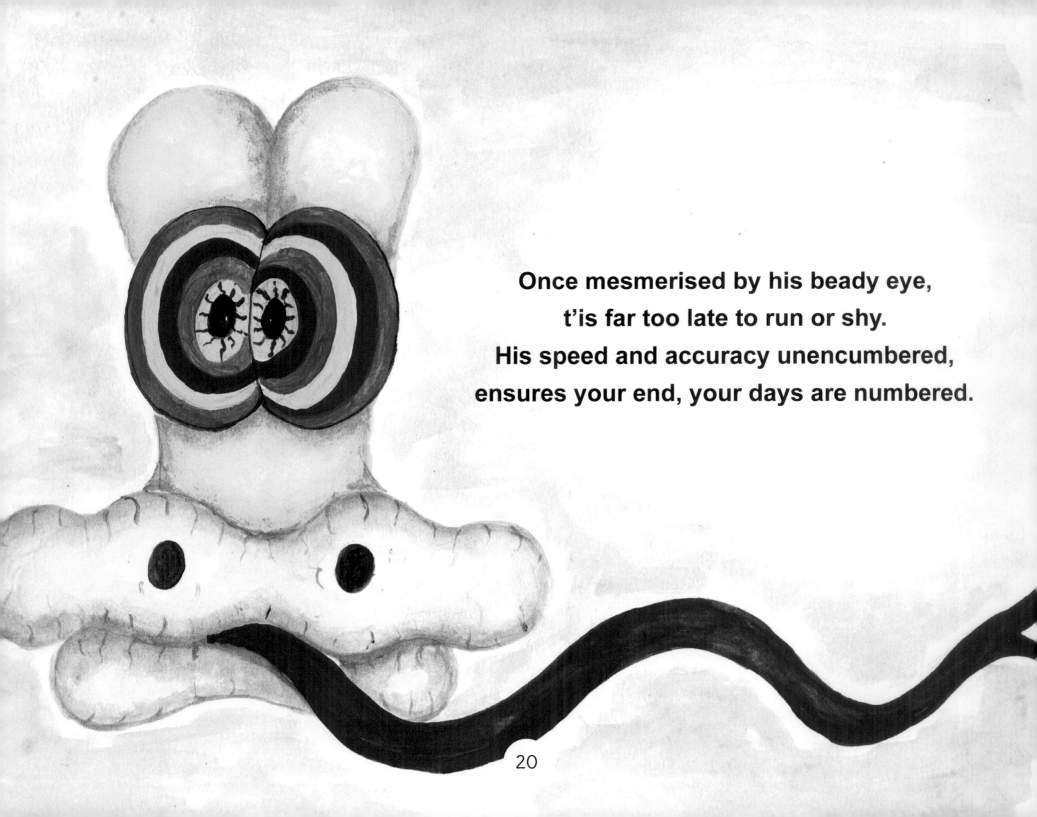

Once mesmerised by his beady eye,
t'is far too late to run or shy.
His speed and accuracy unencumbered,
ensures your end, your days are numbered.

But age as always takes its toll,
his head when reared now
starts to loll.
Still strikes with speed, though
not so fast,
to sink his fang with panting gasp.

Now, with age, his last fang's wobbly.
His food he's always swallowed whole,
but alive inside, it feels so knobbly,
he'll wish for soup and spoon and bowl.

Quick flicking tongue that now does flop.
skin once so smooth but now so crinkly,
his pate all dried, sunburnt on top.
No more a snake, but perhaps a wrinkly.

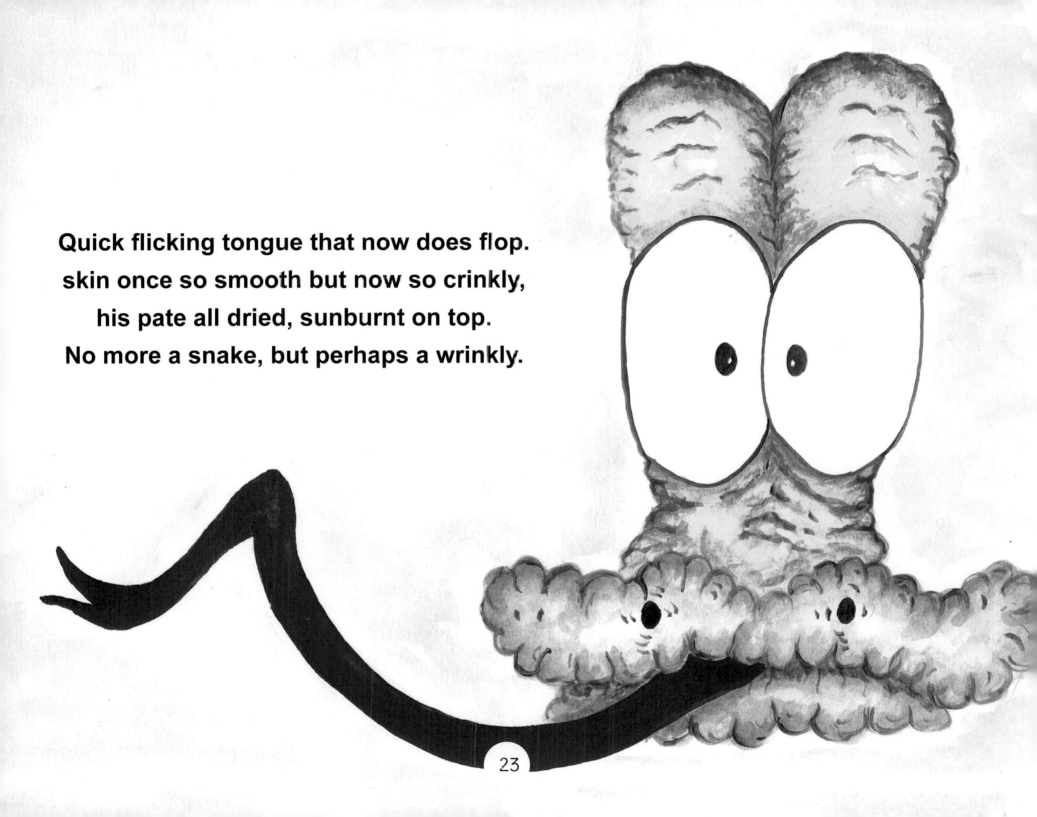

Now age and fate have thus decided,
his remaining days he must be guided.
With care and love, food minced and soft.
Spoon-fed by nurses. Oh, please don't scoff!

24

The home for snakes of many years;
retirement, rest, no fears or tears.
'Twixt bed and chair he'll spend his time,
With pipe and slippers; his eyes will shine.

Mr Parrot's Secret

What's housed within that crooked beak,
his feathers red and green and blue?
One looks more closely when he speaks,
the words so often naughty too.

He likes his food, yes mainly meat,
but seeds and fruit will also do.
Hung upside down from his two feet,
he'll tell you he's not cockatoo.

Of course! he's parrot, with beak like vice
when fed a mouse or perhaps a vole,
his like of fingers is not nice.
Does his stomach digest it whole?

Or maybe just inside his beaky
are rows of short sharp razor teeth.
In which case, he is very sneaky,
He's fooled us all, just like a thief!

But no one dares to peep inside;
the vet he wants his fingers eight.
Who can discover what it hides?
'Tis still the subject of debate.

Robina

Robina the rodent is really a rat,
tailless, part hairless and big as a cat.
Her habits are notorious, her friends
are not many,
beware, our Robina, she cares
not two penny.

She lives in the attic, hid under a tank.
Her nest made from paper, straw
and old plank.
With nocturnal ramblings throughout
her domain,
unchallenged, unworried because
of her fame.

Late at night when she prowls, it
is unmolested.
By dog and by cat she is feared and
detested.
They both bear the scars from a previous meet,
the cat on its ear, the dog on its feet.

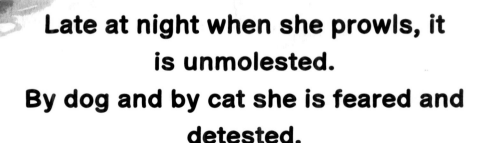

One particular night, on her jaunt nocturnal,
smoke filled her eyes; the smell was infernal.
The danger she spotted to dog and to cat,
from flame and the smoke that
was thick and so black.

From out of the shoebox and
under the chair,
both scared of our rodent, they
were chased up the stairs.
The cat screamed with fear, the dog
yelped and whined.
The family awoke to the
terrible sound.

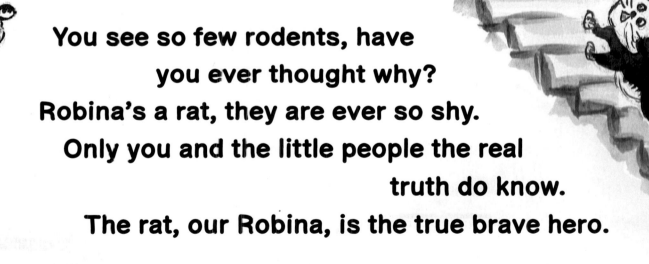

You see so few rodents, have
you ever thought why?
Robina's a rat, they are ever so shy.
Only you and the little people the real
truth do know.
The rat, our Robina, is the true brave hero.